END SMALL TALK

Deep Questions for Better Conversations

CORY STOUT

Production & Art Direction: Saeah Wood

Editorial: Amy Reed

Design & Layout: Ivica Jandrijević

ISBN:
Hardcover: 978-1-955671-22-4
Paperback: 978-1-955671-20-0
E-Book: 978-1-955671-23-1

 OTTERPINE

otterpine.com

This book was created with organic, free-range human neurons. No artificial intelligence was used in the writing of this book.

INTRODUCTION

"Where are you from? Oh, Phoenix? Is it pretty hot there?"

"Yeah, it's hot. But it's not humid, so it's more of a dry heat."

And that's the moment I visualize jumping out of the window, breaking my leg, and limping back into the room just so I can join a different conversation.

THAT'S how much I despise small talk.

4

WORST QUESTIONS OF ALL TIME

- So, how's everything going with you?

- What have you been up to lately?

- Have you heard from [insert name]?

- What do you do?

We have a limited amount of time to learn about our friends, family, lovers, and the strangers we encounter every day. Questions pave the road to understanding and connection. A question is so much more than a simple request for information—it's a bridge between two minds.

In every great conversation, there's a moment when the participants tacitly agree to get real. When we waste our time with small talk, it can take a long time to get to this moment—or we may never get there at all. The questions in this book are designed to help you reach that magical crossover moment, to get out of the shallows of conversation and dive into the depths of connection.

There are lots of books of questions out there, but these are not your typical icebreaker questions. These are original, nuanced, and thoughtful inquiries designed to both help you understand yourself a bit better and get the listener actively engaged.

The questions in this book are rated on a scale of 1 to 10. That doesn't necessarily mean easy to difficult. The higher the number, the deeper the question will be, which will help you and others reveal your most authentic selves. Don't be fooled by multiple choice or yes/no questions. No answer is ever that simple. The follow-up *WHY?* is always implied.

Use these questions with people you love or people you've just met, on a first date or with your partner of several years, with your best friend or the person you're sitting next to on an airplane, at family dinners or drinking beer with friends around a campfire. It is always a good time to get to know people better and deepen your connection with humanity.

Asking questions is how I affect the change I want to see in the world. It is how I find truth, both my own and that of others. I don't care what answers come back, and I don't judge anyone's answers as right or wrong, or good or bad. What matters is encouraging people to examine their belief systems, look honestly at themselves, and share that self with others.

So, here's my first question: What are you waiting for?

THE QUESTIONS

Imagine you're holding a box in your hands. Open the lid. What's in the box?

In the last 10 days, has time seemed to pass faster or slower than usual?

A Rocky Mountain town in Colorado announces a new strain of cannabis called Alpine Stone Dust. Your town also announces their new cannabis strain—
and they put you in charge of naming it.

What do you call it?

Which day of the week
fits your personality?

Which relative
makes the best food
dish? What is it?

What was your favorite pet growing up?

What is your current ring tone? What does it say about you?

Do you know the
first names of any
of your eight great-
grandparents?

Which of these fonts
would you put on
an outgoing letter?
What do you think
that says about you?

HARPER
9630 N. SIERRA DRIVE
VILLA RICA, GA 30180

Heather
7742 Creekside Lane
Hoffman Estates, IL 60169

Jacob Thomas
451 EAST BOHEMIA ST.
MCDONOUGH, GA 30252

Alvin Leonard
2 Inverness Drive
Fort Myers, FL 33905

If you could play
any instrument at a
master level, which
one would it be?

If you estimate all the emails you'll answer in your entire life, are you more than 50% done?

Who owns the right to the space behind the seat on an airplane: the person in front with the button to recline OR the person in back occupying the knee space?

Name five alternative
uses for a brick.

Which season fits your personality?

How many back-and-forth text messages does it take until you think, "We could have figured this out quicker with a phone call"?

Which legendary guitarist would you like to perform a solo at your funeral?

On a scale of 1–10, where
1 = Bob and 10 = ¡Xenon!,
how bold would you like
to be when choosing
a child's name?

Alexander the Great was so great, they called him "Alexander the Great." King Richard I was so brave, they named him "Richard the Lionheart." What will be your epithet?

Someone gives you $10,000,000, immortality, and a turtle—but if the turtle touches you, you die. The turtle always knows where you are and will always be slowly making its way toward you.

What's your plan to live forever?

Where were your old stomping grounds?

What grounds are you currently stomping?

Take out your phone.
What are your top
six most recently
used emojis? Explain
the strangest one.

Would you take a 30% pay cut in exchange for Mondays and Fridays off?

Sir Mix-a-Lot likes big butts and he cannot lie. What do you like so much you cannot lie about it?

What's your favorite
story that involves
a special car?

Who showed you the ropes on the thing you're really into?

Where are you IN YOUR ELEMENT?

When you smell cigarette smoke, your first thought is what?

If you were a cell in the
human body, what type
of cell would you be?

Which would you appreciate more: one handwritten letter or 10 FaceTime calls?

If you could give
one book as a gift to
everyone you know,
what would it be?

Describing it as if
it's a crime, what do
you do for a living?

What phrase did your mom always say while you were growing up?

Is it artistic to steal art?

What cacao percentage
do you prefer in
your chocolate?
Do you think dark
chocolate preference
is a strong indicator of
emotional maturity?

What do you remember about your first solo airplane flight? Where were you going?

How many rowdy
seven-year-olds would
it take to beat you up?

At the end of the day,
is happiness a choice
or an experience?

How many days has
it been since you've
seen the sunrise?

To the best of your ability, explain how a microwave works.

Is the current
generation:

a) too naked,
b) the right amount
of naked, or
c) not naked enough?

Would it be easier
to explain color to a
blind person or music
to a deaf person?

Would you rather have a big house on 10 acres in Wyoming OR 1,000 square feet on the 99th floor overlooking Central Park?

What do you remember
about your high
school graduation?

How many phone numbers do you have memorized? How many addresses?

Would you rather be 12 inches tall or 12 feet tall?

Do you have enough physical space to support your desired level of creativity?

What does your couch
say about you?

Dali traveled with an ocelot; Elvis famously owned a chimpanzee. What exotic animal would you like to accompany you to showcase your personality?

To the best of your ability and with as much detail as possible, explain Einstein's Theory of Relativity.

Who is currently winning the battle between you and your phone? How might you win the war?

Would you support a government tracker that observes poor driving habits and suspends the licenses of the lowest-scoring 1% of drivers?

Of all the cuddling you've done in your life, what percentage were you the big spoon vs. the little spoon?

What seems to
last longer: your
friendships or romantic
relationships?

If you repeated yesterday 365 more times, where would you be a year from now?

Is the story of your life
more like an epic novel
or a book of poems?

What is a wellness
tip that is very
SPECIFIC to you?

Who throws better
parties, the rich
or the poor?

It's your last day on Earth and you get to pick one place to sit for an entire day and watch the world go by. Where do you choose to sit?

If you quit everything
and applied all
your time, talent,
and determination
to becoming a
professional golfer,
COULD you succeed?

What are you trying to communicate by the clothes you're currently wearing?

Are you more Batman (hero), Robin (sidekick), or Alfred (support)?

When you check out
at a coffee shop and
the tip is automatically
filled in for 20%, how
would you describe
this payment feature:
a generous design
or social extortion?

Can you teach someone
how to kiss?

It's your friend's birthday and you go to the best restaurant in town. They order the $100 steak and ask for a side of ketchup. The server informs them that the chef has elected to not offer ketchup with the steak. Your friend is outraged. Do you side with your friend or with the restaurant?

If cities were stocks, which one would you buy? Which one would you sell?

Would you rather
have someone pray
for you every day
for the rest of your
life OR give you one
really great sandwich
right this moment?

79

Is your mind more like a hotel, with lots of ideas coming and going, or is it like a bank vault, with a secure door and a strict deposit policy?

In the art studio of life, do you feel more like the canvas, the paint, or the brush?

Imagine you could only use one type of greeting for the rest of your life. Would you choose:

a) shaking hands,
b) hugging, or
c) bowing?

How many days in
the last 30 did you
make your bed?

What are some relationship GREEN flags?

If someone borrowed
your body for a week,
what special quirks
would you warn them
about ahead of time?

Are you a better or worse version of yourself while on vacation?

Why didn't you quit
social media a year ago?

Do you know the funky chicken? Do you know the electric slide? Do you know how to walk it out? Do you know how to Dougie? Do you know how to floss?

Talent, determination, timing—which combination of TWO do you think gives a person the best chance of being successful?

What's your silly
and outrageous BUT
also semi-serious
dream in life (e.g.,
astronaut, movie star,
basketball player)?

Fill in the blank:
I'm really looking
forward to a time in
my life when _____.

What are you
unapologetically
nerdy about?

Is NOW the best time
in human history to
be really attractive?

How many times have you moved in the last ten years? How many times would you like to move in the next ten years?

What addiction do
you have in common
with the most
people on earth?

If someone decided they no longer wanted to be friends with you, would you rather they break up with you or fade away?

Are you the same person when your cell phone is in your hand as when your cell phone is in another room?

Imagine your thoughts
are like plants. Are
they in neat rows like
a garden or farm? Or
is your mind a forest,
with wild things like
ferns, weeds, and vines?
Or something else?

If your life were a stovetop, which pursuits are on your two front burners?

Which pursuits are on your two back burners?

Who have you learned
the most from but have
never actually met?

Since the internet revolution, has the overall percentage of people who DESERVE their success gone up or down?

When you seek change,
is it easier to act your
way into a new way
of thinking, or think
your way into a new
way of acting?

A homeless man begs you for money and you give him $5. Later, you see him on the sidewalk enjoying a beer. How do you feel about it?

Is your life dictated more by wants, needs, or shoulds?

Is it wise to monetize
your passion?

Are you open to the idea
of an open relationship?

Have you met any
of your heroes?
How was it?

Imagine your life as a soup that's been simmering since youth with four special ingredients:

- a book that shaped your thinking
- a job that helped you build patience

- a person who went out of their way to believe in you
- a city that helped you develop your character

What are your four ingredients?

Are you a good
friend? Are you good
at making friends?
How are these things
different or the same?

Have you spent more time listening or speaking in your life?

Is it okay to believe in something false, as long as that belief helps you or others in some way?

In the movie of your life, do you feel more like the actor, writer, or executive producer?

What is the most revolutionary social movement you have been a part of?

Over the course of
your life, do you think
your name will end
up in the media more
often or less often than
the average person?

Which question do
you get asked much
more often than
you would like?

On a scale of 1–10, with 10 being the most difficult, how hard would it be for you to sit in a room and do absolutely nothing for 90 minutes?

In the current season of your life, which are you doing more of: planting seeds or harvesting fruit?

How many new people
do you meet in an
average week?

You have two goals: having a partner to love, and having a big bank account. Which one is better to pursue FIRST?

What's a stereotypical joke that is often made about people who share your culture?

You can go to the settings on your phone to see how full your storage is. How full is your brain's storage right now?

The 1920s is known
as the Jazz Age and
the 1970s is known
for the counterculture
movement. What
will this decade
be known for?

Bill Bryson writes in his book, *The Body:* "We make the heart the emotional seat of our being, as when we declare that we love someone with all our heart, or profess a broken heart when they abandon us. Don't misunderstand me. The heart is a wonderful organ, fully deserving of our praise and gratitude, but it is not invested even slightly in our emotional well-being." Agree or disagree?

How many miles of Instagram feed do you estimate you've swiped in your entire life?

It's been said that when you're thinking too little you should probably read, and when you're thinking too much you should probably write. Which one should you do right now—read or write?

Why are humans
so interested in
very old things?

Ten years ago, when you had a big night out, what time would you usually get home? Now, when you have a big night out, what time do you get home?

Overall, is your phone a time-saver or a time-thief?

Are you more
skilled or less skilled
than your income
currently reflects?

Do memories of your
exes fill you with
warm nostalgia or
chilly anxiety?

What was your first real
taste of independence?

Do you think relationships last longer when one partner likes the other just a little more?

On a scale of 1–10, with 1 being "It's fine, let's just eat and leave," and 10 being "I'd like to speak with your manager," where do you place yourself on the entitled customer spectrum?

If I were to pray for you,
what should I pray for?

What else could
go right?

What is a more EFFECTIVE motivator— shame or praise?

A credo is defined
as a set of guiding
principles or beliefs.
What is your credo?

If having children was a product on Amazon, what would be the average review score? What would the top result say?

To what degree is
your view of the
world warped by your
own presence in it?
(HINT: You've never
experienced the vibe
of a room that doesn't
have you in it.)

An inside-out orientation sees identity emerging from within and assumes each person has the liberty to forge their own identity, discover their own values, and choose their own life path. An outside-in perspective sees identity shaped by the social rules of

the collective culture
to which a person
belongs; this person is
more focused on their
obligation to family and
community rather than
to themself. On a scale
of 1–10, with 1 being
totally inside-out and 10
being totally outside-
in, where do you fall?

If one extra year at the end of your life was for sale, how much would you be willing to pay for it now?

What do you invest your time in even though it has zero economic value?

Assuming consciousness persists throughout all space and time, what feeling or human experience would you bottle up and carry with you for all of eternity?

You have ten minutes
to prepare a one-
hour lecture for an
attentive audience,
on any topic. What
topic do you choose?

Where were you
FORGED as a
human being?

What's more important
in a relationship:
being the same age as
your partner or being
raised by parents
of the same age?

What makes someone interesting to you? What makes someone boring to you?

Imagine you committed
to one year without
using the internet.
When the year is up,
you find yourself happier
and enjoying your new
systems for navigating
the world. Would going
back to the internet
make your life better?
Would you do it?

What is the best drug in the world? In this case, best means it has the most upside and the least downside.

What common
customs today
might be considered
inhumane by 2100?

At what age did you experience your biggest physical growth spurt? At what age did you have your biggest emotional growth spurt?

Johnny Appleseed was a prolific spreader of apple seeds. You are a spreader of _____ seeds.

(Fill in the blank.)

On a scale of 1–10,
how lucky are you?
(You cannot say 7.)

Would you rather
your kid be the bully
or the bullied?

On a scale of 1–10, how disciplined are you right now? (You cannot say 7.)

What's the most disciplined you've ever been?

Do you believe you have the power to change your number?

On a scale of coffee to cocaine, how addictive is marijuana? Cigarettes? Social media?

Who is most responsible
for the experience of
your life? Who is second
most responsible?

Do you think cheating is more or less prevalent today than it was for your grandparents' generation?

Which TV dad did
you love the most?

Is alcohol your favorite drug? Is it your most consumed drug? Why is that the case?

In what ways does the world pull at you in an attempt to make you NORMAL? How much effort does it take to maintain your distinctiveness?

Do you favor friendships
with a shared past
or a shared future?

When you're going
through a slump,
which do you prefer:

a) comforters,
b) nudgers, or
c) slappers?

What doors are opening for you right now?

In Russian drinking culture, if you break a glass while making a toast, it's a sign that you need to finally DO that thing you've been thinking about doing for a long time. What is that thing for you right now? (Cheers!)

Are there things that
you would like to tell
others, but feel it is too
risky to share? (There
is no pressure to share
those things now if
you're not ready.)

Are you an artist?
Why or why not?

Do you underestimate
or overestimate how
much YOU contribute to
YOUR level of success?

What's your least favorite conversation topic?

Do you believe artists
need to suffer in order
to make good art?

In what ways do you
help the cowboys
sing the blues?

Are you adding to or
subtracting from the
cumulative peace
of humanity?

Has technology created
more independence
or dependence?

"So as not to feel the horrible burden of time that breaks your back and bends you to the earth, you have to be continually drunk. But on what? Wine, poetry, or virtue, as you wish. But be drunk."
—Charles Baudelaire

What are you drunk on?

If you lost your memory,
which three people
would you trust
to reconstruct the
story of your life?

Are you using the internet, or is the internet using you?

What is one thing in life right now that you are pretending not to know?

Who are your top three suppliers? (Of anything, in general.)

Is it possible to become more successful than you ever allowed yourself to imagine?

Should two legally consenting adults be allowed to duel without legal ramifications?

When was the last time you vomited from drinking?

Which has a more
divisive effect on
humanity: religion
or money?

Think about every desire within you. Let's pretend POOF, they are ALL realized. How do you feel now?

If you could design the
perfect afterlife, what
would it look like?

Would you accept
$100/day for the rest of
your life if it meant you
could not feel drunk
or high ever again?

If everyone in the world
was suddenly implanted
with your personality,
what would the world
look like in five years?

Does closure actually
make you feel better?

Is it easy or difficult for you to imagine that when you are very old, you'll be physically attracted to another very old person?

Do you expect life to keep getting better, year after year? Do you have full confidence that next year will be better than last year?

What are the essential characteristics of the place you call home?

Should the love of your life also be the best sex of your life?

What do you wish
people noticed
about you more?

What are you
running toward?

Who has received
the MOST of your
forgiveness?

If 1 is resting on your laurels and 10 is the song "Eye of the Tiger" from *Rocky*, what number are you currently?

There's a new restaurant called Karma. Instead of ordering from the menu, you get what you deserve. So, what are you getting?

One person professes to know everything about love. One person professes to know nothing about love. Which person would you rather marry?

When it comes to
friendship at this point
in your life, are you:

a) looking to hire, or
b) anticipating a
few layoffs?

If you were a life coach and someone handed you your own anonymized file, what would be your first recommendation?

Where did you lose
your virginity?

What privilege do you enjoy the most but definitely don't deserve?

If 0 is "go with the flow,"
a canoe on the river of
life without a paddle,
and 100 is total self-
determination, what
number are you now?

Is FALLING in love more like winning the lottery or learning to play the piano?

Is it okay to consider someone to be YOUR best friend if they don't consider you THEIR best friend? Should all best friending be mutual?

Imagine your life's pursuits are plants in a garden. By the time you realized the garden was YOURS, there were already a lot of things growing—trees, flowers, grass, even weeds. Now, you're the gardener. You get to decide what plants go in it, how big they

get, and the complexity
of the ecosystem—
and you must tend
to it as it grows.

Which plants in your
garden need more
space for growth?
Which ones need to be
pruned back? Which
need to be removed?

When was the last time you were REALLY angry? How did you express it?

Imagine a ladder with 10 rungs. 1 represents the worst possible version of your life. 10 represents the best possible version of your life. Which rung are you currently standing on?

Do you think it's
important to
study history?

When was the last time you slept in the same bed for 60 consecutive days?

One part of your body has just been named "Best Body Part of the Year." Deliver the acceptance speech from the perspective of that body part.

In most human stories, you will encounter the hero, villain, guide, and victim. We embody all these roles to SOMEONE, and various people embody all these roles to US. Who plays each of these archetypes in your life?

What does your "Rich Life" look like? (Inspired by Ramit Sethi)

What's a personal rule that you allow yourself to break occasionally? What's a personal rule that you REFUSE to break?

Assuming the two will rarely happen simultaneously in your life, would you rather be right or liked?

Let's say your partner upgraded their operating system to include "puppet mode." Whenever you activated it, they would do everything you asked for 30 minutes. How many times per week do you estimate you would invoke "puppet mode?"

If it turned out that you were Truman inside *The Truman Show*— you've been starring in a reality show your whole life and everyone you know is an actor— would you be mad? Which casting decisions did the producers get right? What did they get wrong?

As a woman's career improves, do her romantic options expand or contract? What about for a man?

Which of your exes
would you LEAST
like to sit next to on
a five hour flight?

If the afterlife were
a VIP club and you
were the bouncer,
what would be your
entry requirements?

What do you hope
your partner (or future
partner) means when
they say "I love you?"

Agree or disagree: poor
people are essentially to
blame for being poor?

When pain is shared, is it doubled or halved?

What was your deepest
heartbreak experience?
What did it teach you?

Are you doing an EXCELLENT job of taking care of yourself? Why or why not?

I don't want to be perceived as _____, so I overcompensate by _____ing too much.

(Fill in the blanks.)

If your last relationship was a house plant, did it suffer from too much water, not enough water, or perhaps some back-stabbing cactus named Tammy/Tommy?

Word association time! What's the first thing that comes to mind for the following words:

- vitamin
- medicine
- drug
- hard drug?

Which three people
have had the greatest
effect on your personal
philosophy?

Is guilt an EFFECTIVE
tool to prevent
bad behavior?

What are you shocked that you used to believe? Why do you think you were misguided?

What's one good habit
you are trying to add
but for some reason
cannot get to stick?

What's one bad habit you are trying to remove but for some reason cannot quit completely?

Philosopher and writer François de La Rochefoucauld said, "There are some people who would never have fallen in love, if they had not heard there was such a thing." Do you think he's right? Have you dated any of these people?

Do you approach the
game of life more
like a chess player
or a poker player?

If your life suddenly depended on it, how quickly could you make cocaine appear?

Do you think outer beauty is correlated with inner beauty OR are they inversely correlated?

What recent shift in your life was a long time coming? What recent shift in your life appeared suddenly and unexpectedly?

Scientists just discovered how to make people live forever! You've been appointed the Czar of Immortality, but you only have one million doses to administer. What are your selection criteria?

If you could completely redesign the institution of marriage, what would be the new and improved features of Marriage 2.0?

Close your eyes and draw the letter E on your forehead. Did you draw it so you could see it, or so others could see it? What do you think this implies?

Whose relationship advice do you think is more valuable—a marriage counselor's or a divorce attorney's?

What percentage of who you ARE is derived by what you DO?

Why are we so obsessed with how we think things SHOULD be rather than just accepting things the way they really are?

Who would you rather tell your deepest, darkest secrets: your best friend or a stranger at the airport?

Would you rather have
one AMAZING love for
50 straight years or
five AMAZING loves
for 10 years each?

If you walked into
a room containing
everyone you've ever
met, who would you
be looking for?

What are you addicted
to that is perfectly
legal? If that habit
were declared illegal,
would it change your
consumption?

Who was your best friend 10 years ago? Who is your best friend now? Who is most likely to be your best friend 10 years from now?

On a scale of 1–10, how
sure are you about
what is going on in your
freaking life right now?
(You cannot say 7.)

♫ "Whoa, whoa, you got the best of my love" ♫ are catchy love song lyrics by R&B group The Emotions. Who, unfortunately, got the WORST of your love?

On a scale of 1–10,
if 1 is a completely
dusty mirror and 10 is
a crystal-clear mirror,
how accurately do
you see your true self
when you look in your
mirror? What version
do you show others?

If every promise kept represents a deposit, and every failed promise represents a withdrawal, what is the current balance in your personal bank account?

a) intelligent
b) kind
c) beautiful
d) rich
e) great in bed

Which THREE of these attributes do you choose for your life partner?

257

If you killed someone,
would your best friend
help you bury the body?

Do you make more
decisions based
on love or fear?

One of the cells in your body realizes it is just one tiny component of a greater being. It thinks you are God. It asks you very politely, "God, how would you like to be worshiped?" How do you answer?

What are you
running from?

In our pursuit of mastery, we often inhabit one of three characters: The Dabbler, known for getting very excited about a new training, buying lots of equipment, then losing interest at the first real grind; The Obsessive, who tries so hard that they burn themselves out quickly; or The Hacker, who finds a shortcut to competency, then stays on a plateau because they don't want to do the REAL work. Which of the three best describes you?

What do you do more—THINK with your FEELINGS or FEEL with your THOUGHTS?

"What do you despise? By this you are truly known." —Frank Herbert, *Dune*

What do YOU despise?

Do you fall in love easily?
Why or why not?

Do you have a plan
in place for the
end of your life?

If you were not allowed
to meet new people,
which one of your exes
would you choose
as a life partner?

On a scale of 1–10, how much are YOU in charge of the ways you change?

Netflix, Spotify, Pinterest, or Pornhub: Which company's algorithm would you trust the most to choose your next partner?

Is the most
transformative
psychedelic experience
of your life ahead of
you or behind you?

Variable outcome systems are shown to hook people by delivering rewards in unpredictable patterns, leaving users craving more. (Think slot machines and Instagram.) If you are a good person with good intentions, would it be MORAL to utilize

variable outcome
theory to "hook" a
potential partner?

Adam Smith said,
"The desire for food
is limited in every
man by the narrow
capacity of the human
stomach, but the desire
for the conveniences
and ornaments of
building, dress, and
household furniture
seems to have no limit
or boundary." What

annual salary SHOULD
fulfill the necessities of
life where you live?

Is love measured more by how much two people contribute to each other's happiness, or by their capacity to sacrifice for each other?

Do things mostly
happen for a reason?
Or is the universe
mostly indifferent?

Are you "good" at love?

Share something
that no one else
knows about you.

Which do you value more in a close friend: honesty or loyalty?

"Who cares? One day I'll be dead and no one will remember me anyway." Does this quote give you existential relief or existential anxiety?

Have you ever
walked away from a
relationship while you
were still in love?

If you could communicate with your six-year-old self and tell them not to blame themselves for events that are happening outside of their control, what event would you be talking about?

If you were a teenager in 1930's Germany, what are the chances you would have been a Nazi? If you were a rich landowner in the American South in the 1800s, what are the chances you would have owned slaves?

What do you believe
will happen after you
die? Do you think
anybody really KNOWS?

What belief do you hold
very strongly? What's
the best argument
against that belief?

If you were to die suddenly and meet your maker, would you be proud of the life you've led? What would be your biggest regret?

Hi, I'm Cory Stout, and I'm an optimist. I'm also a writer based in Venice Beach, California, which is mainly where I thought of these questions. I was treasurer of the student council in third grade, and I'm the owner and captain of Woodies sunglasses. My favorite philosopher is Socrates.